Edited by Yu Zhongzheng
          Cao Changguang
Translated by Lin Wusun
              Zhang Qingnian

The Silk Road in Cartoons

Stories from the Dunhuang Murals (4)

新世界出版社
NEW WORLD PRESS

First Edition 2017

By Yu Zhongzheng and Cao Changguang
Translated by Lin Wusun and Zhang Qingnian
Cover Design by Guo Lei

ISBN 978-7-5104-6132-3

Published by
NEW WORLD PRESS
24 Baiwanzhuang Street, Beijing, 100037, China

Distributed by
NEW WORLD PRESS
24 Baiwanzhuang Street, Beijing, 100037, China
Tel: 86-10-68995968
Fax: 86-10-68998705
Website: www.nwp.com.cn
E-mail: nwpcd@sina.com

Printed in the People's Republic of China

Stories from the Silk Road

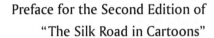

Preface for the Second Edition of "The Silk Road in Cartoons"

Yu Zhongzheng

The "One Belt and One Road" Initiative proposed by President Xi Jinping refers to the building of a "Silk Road Economic Belt" and a "21st Century Maritime Silk Road." This great initiative has received positive reaction, participation and support from nearly half of the countries and regions of the world. It envisages a community featuring political trust, economic integration, cultural inclusiveness as well as shared interests, destiny and responsibility under economic globalization. The "One Belt and One Road" Initiative represents the trend of the times with concepts such as peace, development, and win-win cooperation. It has given great impetus to the integrated development of the Chinese economy alongside the global economy.

The Silk Road was a network of trade, cultural exchange, and friendship and cooperation routes that linked China and the rest of Asia, Europe, Africa and other parts of the world. Gansu Province was the golden passageway and a center of economic and cultural exchange on the Silk Road and a place where the distinctive Silk Road science and culture took shape. To promote and rejuvenate the culture and spirit of the Silk Road, the Silk Road Association of Gansu Province has decided to use its resources to publish a book series telling domestic and foreign readers about the Silk Road and the stories behind it.

Under the tutelage of Cao Changguang, cartoonist and deputy secretary general of the Silk Road Association of Gansu Province, a galaxy of famous cartoonists from Gansu and other provinces were invited to conduct field research, inspection and visits and hold seminars along the Silk Road. In a little more than two years, established cartoonists including Wang Fuyang, Miao Yintang, Chang Tiejun, Xu Jin, Pei Guangduo, and Su Lang completed a cartoon series in seven volumes which was published in Chinese, English and Japanese by Chinese Literature Press in 1994. The title of the book was *The Silk Road in Cartoons*, which goes in four parts, namely, History of the Silk Road, Dunhuang in Pictures, Legends along the Silk Road, and Stories from the Dunhuang Murals. The portrayal of history, historical figures, religion, art, stories, and legends concerning the Silk Road, enriched and seasoned with knowledge, fun and humor, brings readers into a wonderland of imagination and reality. After its publication, *The Silk Road in Cartoons* became popular worldwide and won a number of awards in China. Collected by individuals and in libraries of Japan, Germany, the US and some Southeast Asian countries, the series has played a positive role in promoting the Silk Road culture.

The New World Press' reprint of the series in Chinese, English and Japanese is certainly something to be applauded, appreciated and celebrated. The trilingual publication will certainly strengthen cultural exchange and development between China and countries along the Silk Road and give boost to the joint and comprehensive development of the economy and culture of the "One Belt and One Road" countries along the Silk Road.

The purpose of promoting a nation's past glory is to pave the way for its future glory. I believe that, under the framework of the "One Belt and One Road" Initiative, China's drastic development of economic construction will certainly bring about the flourishing of its culture and art.

June 2016

Contents

The Prince Enters the Womb Riding an Elephant

Cartoons by Zhang An

Siddhartha Learns to Be a Scholar-Warrior

Cartoons by Zhang An

The prince was looked after by his aunt.

Poor worm!

The king built special palaces for his son.

He selected beautiful girls to play with the prince.

Siddhartha soon got tired of all this.

Your Majesty, the Crown Prince has reached the studying age.

Grotto 290 (Northern Zhou)

How Siddhartha Picks
His Wife and Concubine

Cartoons by Zhang An

The crown princes of eight countries have sought her hand but they were all rejected by her.

We're a small country. A political marriage between us won't do justice to you.

Let's put it off for the time being.

Put it off until later? My son's already seventeen.

I recommend you read this book.

031

Grotto 61 (Five Dynasties)

Story of a Pagoda in Khotan

Cartoons by Wang Fuyang

The Story of the Sandalwood Statue of Buddha

Cartoons by Wang Fuyang

There was once a sandalwood statue of Sakyamuni while he was still alive.

After the Buddha's Nirvana, the statue flew from India to Khotan.

The local people ignored it.

Years later.

The seventh night.

Sand buried the city.

They reached Bhima city.

The statue flew there too.

The city of Bhima built a pagoda and temple for the statue.

How King Asoka Built 84,000 Pagodas

Cartoons by Sun Yizeng

Grotto 98 (Five Dynasties)

Uttara Writes on His Skin as if It Were Paper

Cartoons by Sun Yizeng

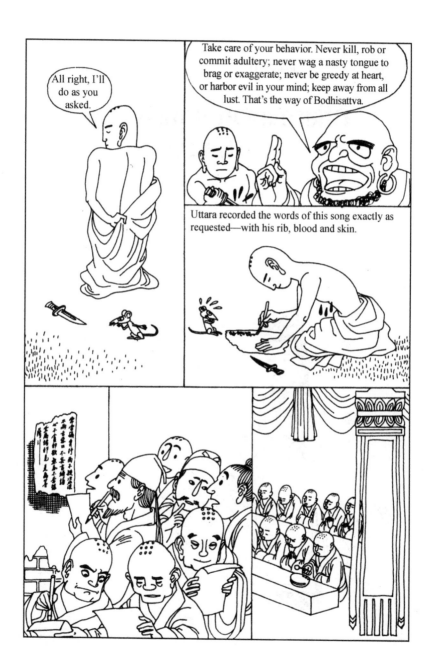

Dharmagan Jumps into a Fire Pit

Cartoons by Sun Yizeng

The son of the King Brahma was named Dharmagan.

What's the right way to save the people from their sufferings?

The Crown Prince was deeply concerned about the bitterness of life in this world.

His sincerity moved Sovereign Sakra.

Who wants to listen to the Buddhist teachings?

The gods in Heaven were moved to tears.

The flowers they dropped fell on the Crown Prince.

King Shetou Luo Jianning Transforms into a Fish to Feed the Famine Victims

Cartoons by Zhu Genhua

One night, the planet Mars appeared in the sky.

King Shetou Luo Jianning ruled the country with magnanimity.

I am wronged!

What can we do now?

The astronomer declared this was a bad omen, foretelling twelve years of continuous drought.

Make an inventory of the warehouses. Control the use of grain.

Royal Edict

Warehouse No. 1

No. 2

No. 3

No. 4

Grotto 85 (Late Tang)

The Story of Vaisali

Cartoons by Zhu Genhua

Grotto 428 (Northern Zhou)

The Single-Antler Immortal

Cartoons by Zhu Genhua

Deep in the mountains of Benares lived an immortal.

He urinated on the grasses on mid-autumn night.

The mother deer ate the grass.

I'll take you to your father.

She later gave birth to a boy.

What a lovely child!

The boy grew up with an antler on his head and feet like those of a deer.

He studied with the immortal.

One day, while climbing the mountain, he slipped and hurt himself in the rain.

His curses so frightened the Dragon King that he dared not rain any more.

The Single-Antler Immortal dined and wined, and enjoyed himself in the palace.

But he soon got tired of it.

We've had plenty of rain. You may return to the mountain if you wish.

The Single-Antler Immortal returned to the forests. This time he knew what he really wanted.

Grotto 98 (Five Dynasties)

The Adventures of Danniki

Cartoons by Zhu Genhua

Brahman Danniki was a poor peasant.

One year, there was a bumper harvest.

He borrowed an ox from a neighbor to carry back the ripened crops.

Okay.

Here's your ox.

The ox went out of the village for a drink. But he was stolen by a cattledealer who happened to pass by.

图书在版编目（CIP）数据

　　漫画丝绸之路. 敦煌壁画故事. 四 = The Silk Road in Cartoons: Stories from the Dunhuang Murals 4 : 英文 / 于忠正，曹昌光编 ；林戊荪等译. -- 北京 ：新世界出版社，2017.4
　　ISBN 978-7-5104-6132-3

　　Ⅰ. ①漫… Ⅱ. ①于… ②曹… ③林… Ⅲ. ①漫画一连环画一作品集一中国一现代 Ⅳ. ①J228.2

　　中国版本图书馆CIP数据核字(2016)第323737号

The Silk Road in Cartoons: Stories from the Dunhuang Murals (4)
漫画丝绸之路：敦煌壁画故事（四）

出　　品：王君校
策　　划：张海鸥
作　　者：于忠正　曹昌光
译　　者：林戊荪　等
英文定稿：李淑娟
英文校对：Paul Adams
责任编辑：李淑娟　董　莹
封面设计：郭　磊
责任印制：李一鸣　黄厚清
出版发行：新世界出版社
社　　址：北京西城区百万庄大街24号（100037）
发行部：(010) 6899 5968　(010) 6899 8705（传真）
总编室：(010) 6899 5424　(010) 6832 6679（传真）
http://www.nwp.cn
http://www.newworld-press.com
版权部：+8610 6899 6306
版权部电子信箱：nwpcd@sina.com
印刷：北京京华虎彩印刷有限公司
经销：新华书店
开本：850mm×1160mm　1/32
字数：50千字　　印张：3.625
版次：2017年4月第1版　2017年4月北京第1次印刷
书号：ISBN 978-7-5104-6132-3
定价：28.00元